M000035737

Oh Yeah,
Blessed!

Printed and Bound in the USA

ISBN: 978-0- 9972605-1- 9

First Edition First Printing

Written by Allison Minor-Green

Illustrations and Cover Design by Tyrus Goshay

Scriptures taken from The New Living Translation Bible and

The New King James Version Bible

Dedication

First of all I would like to thank my Father in Heaven for giving me this Godly task. I am so humbled that He would think so much of me, to allow me to carry out this most delicate task to the most precious souls there are, children. If we instill in them His principles while they are young they will not depart from His Word. They may stray, but His Word, His pull on their heart & His purpose for their life will never depart! I would like to dedicate this book to my most awesome husband Cecil who kept pushing me to complete this book and believed in me from conception to delivery. I would also like to thank my parents Byron "Tank" and Viana Minor, my niece Ambria Minor, my siblings Marisa & Johnathan and my pastor Allen W. Ben for all of your help and for being my test audience. Thank you Apostle Lawrence D. Hardy, you prophesied this book to me September 7, 2014, unbeknownst to you, that several months earlier I told Cecil what God had laid upon my heart to do. That's God!

Habakkuk 2:2- Then the Lord answered me and said: "Write the vision and make it plain on tablets, that he may run who reads it."

1 Thessalonians 5:20- Do not despise prophecies.

Peacefully Yours,
Allison Minor- Green

"Let all the Blessed people in the house say Amen," said Pastor

Everyone in the church began to yell out Amen. Amen came from the balcony, Amen came from the choir. Amen even came from the piano and the drums. Even the children in the church participated.

"Did you enjoy children's church today Niece?"

"I sure did," said Niece.

"Well, what did you learn?" said Nanny.

GOD

While holding up the picture she so beautifully colored, Niece stated, "I learned that God loves me thiiiiiiis much and that He lives in my heart."

"He sure does" said Nanny, "let's head home."

Nanny was so happy. She was finally able to finish washing the dishes, a task she absolutely disliked, before her fingers got totally wrinkled. She shouted out

"Thank you Lord, I'm Blessed!"

AUNTS
Like Moms Only
Cooler

Niece saw Nanny finally finish folding that mountain of clothes she has had stacked up for weeks and right when she put the last item away she saw Nanny dancing and heard her singing, "Thaaank Yooou Lord, I'm Blessed, Thank You Lord, I'm Blessed, Thaaank Yooou Looord, I'm-m-m-m Blessssed!"

Niece couldn't figure out why Nanny would always say, "Thank You Lord, I'm Blessed" all the time and frankly, it was driving her crazy.

Niece thought Nanny was weird.

"Hey Niece, would you like to go to the store with me?" said Nanny

"Sure," said Niece

They hopped in the car, made sure to buckle their seatbelts, tuned the radio to Kidz 92.5FM and headed out to their favorite store, T & V Grocery Mart.

On the way to the store, Nanny and Niece were almost hit by a big blue truck that was traveling on the wrong side of the street. Nanny swerved out of the way to avoid the accident and thankfully all was well.

Nanny immediately yelled out, "Thank You Lord, We're Blessed!"

This angered Niece and she yelled out, "No Nanny, we're lucky! Lucky that that big blue truck didn't hit us!"

Nanny smiled and said, "No, Niece, we're blessed. You see, when you are blessed you have an extra special protection on you. Being blessed protects you from things that could hurt you, just like that truck that could have hurt us. Being blessed also reminds us of God's love; we should thank God for His blessings everyday. You see, Niece, luck is temporary, being blessed lasts forever!"

Niece took some time to think about what it must feel like to

have extra special protection.

That would be awesome, thought Niece.

That night, Niece was preparing with Nanny for her oral spelling test. She did not get much studying done, but she was determined to get a good grade tomorrow on the test.

Test Today!

The next day at school it was time for the oral spelling test.

Niece sat quietly in her desk while the other students spelled their word aloud.

Niece thought, this will be easy, I'll get a good grade no doubt.

It was time for Niece to spell her word, The teacher said, "your word is, Helper."

Miss Nia Peeps
17/328

Niece didn't remember helper being on her spelling word list but still gave it a try. She thought, and she thought, and she thought, took a deep breath, and she began to spell the word, H-E- L-P- E-R.

It came out perfect!

"Correct," said the teacher, "you correctly spelled the mystery word. You get an A!"

Niece was so happy.

Miss Nia Peeps

She closed her eyes, smiled and tried to remember

just what Nanny would say at a time like this and remembered,

"Oh Yeah, Thank You Lord, I'm Blessed!"

You Are Blessed!

1. Name two things in your life that tell you that you are blessed.

2. Would you rather be lucky or blessed? Why?

Parents/Guardians/Teachers:

Read the study scriptures aloud to your child(ren)/students to

further the discussion about being blessed.

Deuteronomy 28:2-6, NLT

About the Author:

Allison Minor-Green is a new author, Oh Yeah Blessed, is her first book and many more are to follow. Green has also written several inspirational columns for her college newspaper while serving as that pages editor. When Green is not writing she is practicing as a Certified Pediatric Nurse Practitioner (CPNP).

ad_minor@hotmail.com

The illustrator

Tyrus goshay is a digital illustrator and 3d artist with over 16 years of experience. He serves as a college professor, teaching both game design, and illustration in his off time. Tyrus has his bachelors in computer animation and Multimedia, and his masters degree in teaching with technology (malt). He has contributed to several award-winning projects in the world of toy design and has been recognized for his achievements in academia as well. He also has tutorials in illustration and Digital sculpting available for training on the web.

Feel free to visit him and his team at www.Tgosketchillustration.Com

Facebook.Com/tgosketch

Instagram/tgosketch

Made in United States
Orlando, FL
01 November 2022